SHORTPACKED!™ PULLS THE DRAMA TAG

The second Shortpacked! collection
by David Willis

Shortpacked! can be found online at www.shortpacked.com.

This book is dedicated to
Superbook, which taught me that anything
can be a family-friendly story, no matter how
much it's actually about incest.

What I'm saying is, if *I* were adapting Genesis 24 for kids, I'd probably leave out the whole cousin angle.

On the other hand, they do tell us in another episode that one of their kids grows up to be a thuggish, hairy beastman, so at least that's a clear message about the genetic consequences.

Introduction

Welcome to the second *Shortpacked!* collection.
In the first book, I had the most awesome
foreword ever, written by the deliciously insane
Greg Killmaster. In Book 2, it's just me. I'd sent
all sorts of e-mails to Batman, asking if he'd do me this favor, but I never
heard one peep out of him. What a jerk.

Now that you've already gotten the first book (you'd have better!) and now
have in your hands the second, I'll let you in on something. The first book
was crap. What a waste! This second book is where stuff really kicks into
gear. All of my favorite stories are in this book, and all of the stuff in the old
book is for chumps.

This truth will hold until I need to sell the third book.

Just like in the first book, there's short commentary by me underneath the
comics on all of these pages. But you'll also notice that on page ten, Robin
begins typing. I thought I'd have her add some context to the stories you're
about to read from her own point of view. *But how can this be*, you may
ask, *she is fictional!*

Well, yes, she is. And I have a very lengthy explanation for how I could
summon her from her own comic strip world to write about her own universe... without breaking the fourth wall.

I swear I do.

But it's in my other pants.

--David Willis

If there's a hand-sketched doodle on this page, that means you either bought yourself the coveted, limited *Shortpacked! Extra!* version of this book, you came to see me at a convention, or I just think you're sexy.

Robin's Introduction

My name is **Robin Angela DeSanto**,
an' this is *totally* my retrospective.

That's right. I put one of those apostro-
thingers at the end of my "and." That's just
how I roll. Some might say that's a little bit
wonky, since I'm typin' this out an' all, an'
so my usual flair for casually-abbreviated
English would normally go all untypeified.

See, that's 'zactly why I gotta *do* it. I gotta be me. You gotta be able to feel
the Robinness flow from my fingertips, into the computer, past the porn, and
onto the page. It's how you *know* it's me. Otherwise, it just ain't, y'know?

For example, I could have begun with this:

   ROBIN'S LOG - (Oh my God, that totally sounds like poop.)

That's how my sister woulda started it. She's something of a copro...?
copra...? *poopophile*. Or at least she was when she was ten. We haven't
spoken for a while. Lemme Google her.

Aw jeez.

Or imagine if Amber were writing it:

   *HAY I LIK COMPUTORS MY NAME IS AMBER AND I HAVE A LOT OF
   PONIES. WILL YOU BE MY FRIEND? IF YOU DO I WILL JUST PUSH
   YOU AWAY. I NEED TO LOSE WEIGHT.*

And guess the likely author of this opening:

   I'm Batman.

Here's a hint. It was *Bruce Wayne.* I know! His secret's totally blown.

Anyway, this was Robin, fo' shizzle. Expect to see more from me soon.

Word out.

Shortpacked! daily strips

You know, I think Ethan just might be gay.

It's just a theory.

One time, my laptop broke. I wish I could have whored myself to get it fixed, but for some reason that doesn't seem to be an option for males. Straight males, anyway.

Girls have things so easy!

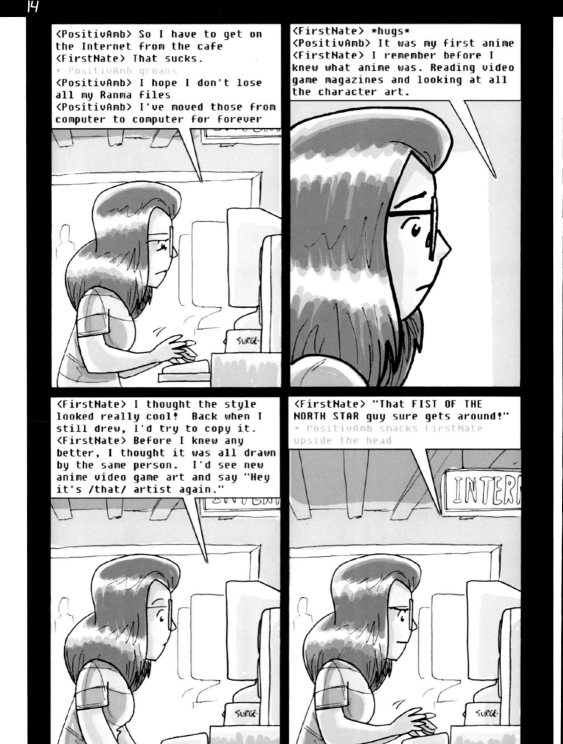

Confession time. I drew this strip before the one prior. I realized Amber has a laptop, not a desktop, and, not wanting to redraw it, edited it so she looks like she's in a lab and added some text about her breaking her laptop.

Then I drew the previous strip and began a storyline. Laziness works in weird ways.

Amber and I are of one mind on this. It's part of how I justify buying so many action figures.

Amber is chasing my girlfriend Maggie and me on our first dating anniversary.

She's kind of a foulmouth, in case you haven't noticed.

I facepalm every single time some dude on the Internet complains about how new "kiddi-fied" G.I. Joe toys aren't as cool as the "original" G.I. Joe, where "original" G.I. Joe means "the stuff twenty years into the franchise that the fans of the original line hate because it's so kiddie."

BOTCON 2005 strips

BotCon 2005 was the first Transformers convention run by Brian Savage's Fun Publications. New authority figures are hated by default. Such is the way of things.

Brian Savage does indeed hate peace and love, but these days, I'm much better at spinning that as a positive.

BOTCON 2005 strips

BotCon 2005 was full of things that apparently went well for the G.I. Joe convention, but really fell flat with some Transformers fans. One such thing was Gambling Night. Gambling Night must go over great with G.I. Joe fans, but taking five minutes to lose the ten chips given to me and then being done for the night? Kind of a waste. BotCon 2006 did not have Gambling Night.

BOTCON 2005 strips

And now that restraining order is framed.

BOTCON 2005 strips

There couldn't have been more than 300 people at BotCon 2005. The next years improved incredibly, but that first year was such a misfire. Nicely organized, though.

This strip is a fraction of a longer, epic saga me and my friend Graham came up with. Somehow, Batman sends the atmosphere-destroying missile to another universe to keep it out of Superman's hands. But in this "other universe," Spider-Man's Aunt May ends up with the atmosphere-destroying missile, turns malevolent, and Batman has to cross timelines to stop her. I'm sure dinosaurs with flamethrowers were also involved.

CLUMP SOUL

Yo, it's Robin again.

Don't ask me what goes on inside the depraved mind of Amber O'Malley. Sometimes she hides behind the customer service counter all effin' day, starin' up into the scaffoldin', thinkin' of who knows what.

Probably her "boyfriend." Y'know, the fake kind of boyfriend. The *Internet* kind.

Do you know what you do with real boyfriends? You get dinner. You go to see movies. You totally make out on the couch. But with "boyfriend"s? You stay up all night typing *LOL* and *hugs* at 'em. Lemme recreate a typical "boyfriend"/"girlfriend" conversation:

```
<girlfriend> i m so lonely
<boyfriend> hay i m a loser who cant get real girls
<girlfriend> ^.^
<boyfriend> omfg
<girlfriend> it is i a girl
<boyfriend> i will reciprocate your emasculating
       anime-style emoticons in
        the hopes that i can get in your e-pants
<girlfriend> ^.^
<boyfriend> also i have girl feelings
<girlfriend> even tho i am extremely fat lets cyber
```

It's sickening. Well, ya gotta get it where ya can, I guess.

(Amber can't get it.)

I was still experimenting with colors during this storyline. You have no idea how frustrating it is to color a big ball of random junk using a limited palette (48 colors or less) for file size reasons.

These days, I just say "screw it" and save the damn thing to 128 colors.

All I can think of, looking back on these strips, is how big of a pain in the ass these were to color.

When I was a small child, I had this puzzle of the United States. I'd take out all the pieces, and one by one, I'd trace them on paper, ending up with a toddler-drawn map. I would do this over and over.

Cartography is awesome.

Haha! I forgot that the Katamari in the first panel was just big clumps of states. That's pretty neat.

I should be a cartoonist or something.

I do what Ethan does, but I don't draw out the map. I keep it all in my head, and it updates as I don't find things and need to add new destinations as desperation increases.

You know you've had a bad night when your last stop is Meijer. You have to be really desperate to go to Meijer.

I get emails asking me if I'm like this. The answer is yes.

Oh god, yes.

And Robin is right. My girlfriend Maggie swoons over that look in my eye where I'm completely dedicated to some insane, pointless obsession she doesn't understand. Apparently that's sexy. But not sexy enough that nerds get laid all the time. Hmm.

Ooooh, hey, look, it's *Cybertron* Hot Shot! Man, my backgrounds used to be so detailed.

That slow metamorphosis in color style I mentioned a few pages ago? This is where it ended. Soft colors that don't overwhelm the lineart, and nobody's dying of skin cancer.

FEAR-MONGERING

I always knew our fearless leader, Galasso, was a little off. Sure, he's kinda a megalomaniacal dictator-like crazyman, who rules our store with an iron fist. That's to be friggin' expected. This is retail, y'know.

But when he started payin' close attention to the doin's of Pat Robertson, that's when you knew somethin' was afoot.

(Mind, he ain't chuggin' Galasso-brand health shakes yet, so we may all yet be safe.)

To his credit, he at least tried goin' about it in a unique way. Historically, products sales were helmed by tiny wannabe Pat Robertsons, creating mass scares to lead people back to their own products. But this is the Internet age. People crucify Pat Robertsons in the safety of their own home, in mass numbers on message boards, an' sound their rhetorical support in the direction of the demonized.

So why not create a Pat Robertson who's against everythin' you want to sell, rile up the Intermanets, an' anger peeps back into your realm of business in spiteful retaliation?

Of course, no real effect is caused by the Internets, 'cuz everyone's too busy railin' against Pat Robertsons on their computers. Meanwhile, real folks are off buyin' Pat Robertson-brand health shakes.

So close, Galasso! So close!

Now, if we'd just advertise my fine ass, we'd be rakin' in the dough.

When you're a Scientologist, and your baby is choking on a toy's spring-loaded missile, it's like, wow, because you *know* you're the only one who can help.

I don't use Geoffrey Nicholson nearly enough. Who else will tell me sweet, frightening lies to keep me on a moral path?

God, I hate Fox News.

I was really sad when the Transformers movie came and went without giving us an Optimus Prime riding a motorcycle. What the hell kind of movie property doesn't give us somebody riding a motorcycle? One that botches all its Academy Award nominations, that's what kind.

This is one of those strips where it helps if you watch the same retarded television shows I do. Sadly, not even most Transformers fans could stand to watch through much of *Transformers Cybertron*.

Suffice to say, Dr. Lucy Suzuki is a crackpot.

I drew this strip in a terrible rush while waiting in an airport for my flight.

This is how I rationalize its terribleness.

Fist AIDS is a very real affliction that our government refuses to acknowledge because its coffers are filled by the fat cats of Big Fisting.

I, uh, only ever bought one Xevoz set. And it wasn't until after the toyline was cancelled. Basically, I'm yelling at myself in this strip.

Ethan learns how to fill his gaping hole soon enough.

This is one of those strips that came into being from watching movies and inserting my own witty interjections, and then realizing that they must be immortalized.

On the Internet, you're never alone. Even if you're turned on by, say, potato chips. There are other chiposexuals, and they have fanfic.

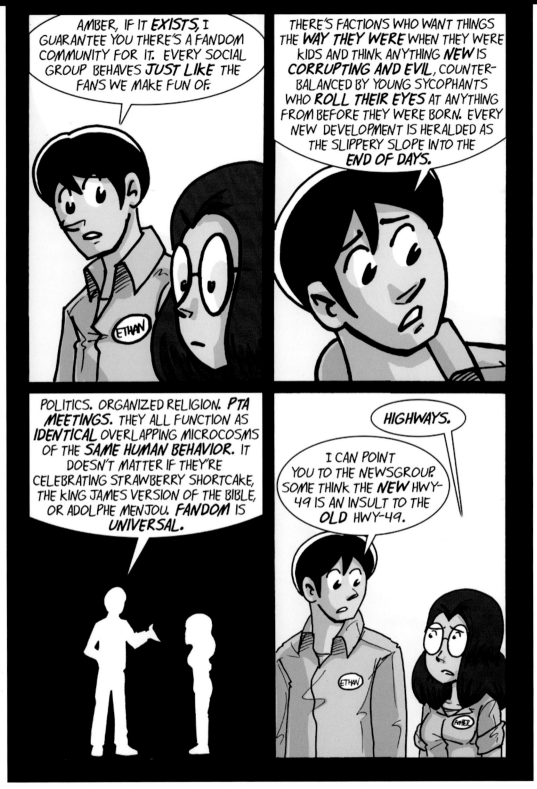

I am not joking. This community exists.

Kup and I had so many good times together. There was that time I was driving to Wizard World Chicago and the exhaust system fell out from under us while passing through Dayton. And then there was that time the door wouldn't close while driving home for Christmas and the insides of all the windows iced over and I hit a snow embankment and had to get towed off of it. Sweet memories.

They're still trying to sell these sets.

If BotCon really wanted to preserve my "investment," they'd clearance them until they all sold out, so the going price could in some way rise. By refusing to clearance them (or destroy the remaining sets), they're ensuring that the secondary market price will never ever increase. But, again, thankfully I don't really care. I just find it amusing.

I've heard from readers that this strip now adorns the employee break rooms of various retail stores. Perhaps it speaks truth to power.

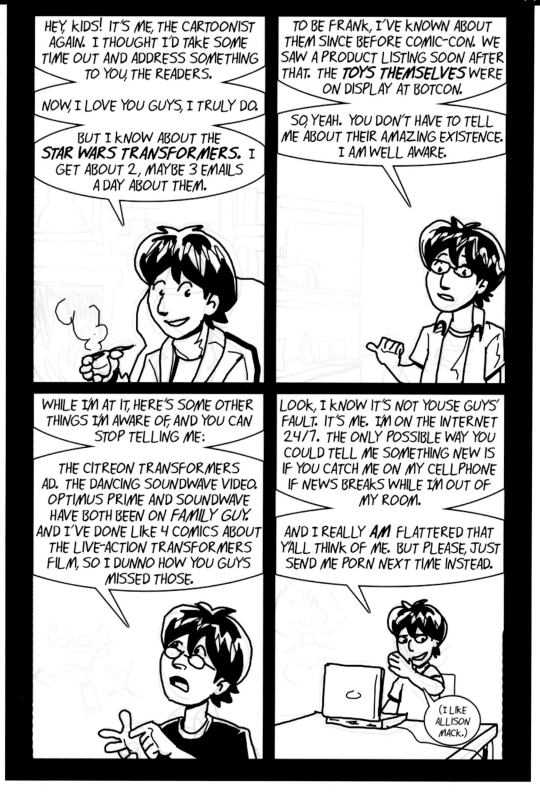

I still get emails about those damn *Star Wars Transformers*. Oh, and apparently there's this origami Movie Bumblebee made out of KFC buckets.

Did you know there's this guy who fought in Iraq who legally changed his name to Optimus Prime?

The less I say about this, the better.

(TOMORROW.)

I wonder how large Destro's chiropracty bills are.

FAZTIVUS

So there's this kid, right?

Y'know, I had a pretty sweet deal goin' on at Shortpacked!. I gotta roommate outta the deal, found some hot dude to crush over an' inevitably seduce, an' I can even get sagely advice from a former President of the United States.

But then it's Christmas season and we get in those seasonal hires, and we get this kid named Faz. Oh Cheese, you just wanna just punch him in the effin' face.

The kid think he's, like, God's gift to women. Dammit, doesn't he know that *I'm* God's gift to women? And men. Mostly men. But sometimes chicks. They can't resist staring at my womanly girl things. Y'know how it goes.

(Once when I was totally eating some sorta marshmallow/steak sauce sandwich, Amber just couldn't take her eyes offa me. What is with that? She hasn't ever had a real boyfriend, so you do the math.)

Anyway, this Faz kid. So obnoxious. He enters a room an' expects everyone to worship him, as if he's some great whatchamacallit. It's seriously pissin' me off, 'cuz he's robbin' *my* spotlight. Dammit, I don't maintain these glorious gams for nothin'.

The worst part? He's so unaware of how self-centered he is.

Hey, look, it's the introduction of Faz! Everybody loves Faz. He's always so smiley.

I will never live down this punchline. It was so terrible the Earth opened up to swallow cities whole, marriages were ruined, and *Arrested Development* was pulled off the air.

I'm starting to think *Shortpacked!* has something against selling insurance for toys in lieu of real customer service, and that rewarding one over the other causes problems in the workplace.

When I worked shifts at Toys "R" Us, often every sales floor employee had the bike aisle assigned to their rounds. If one were caught somewhere else, they were redirected back to the bike aisle.

What a nightmare.

I'd just like to say that either Galasso's head is really tiny in that first panel, or he has the manliest shoulders ever documented.

Faz used to be a lot smarter.

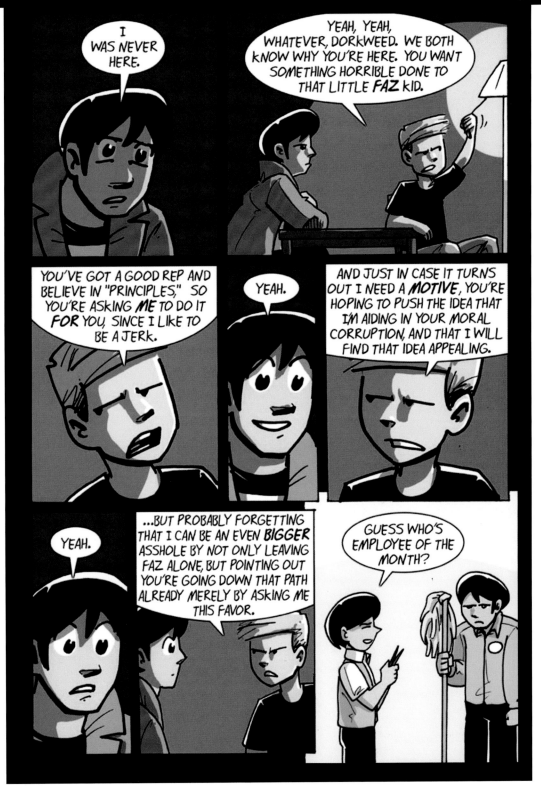

I like showing chinks in Ethan's moral solidarity. He likes to think he's the ethical center for the group, which is a really jerky thing to think, but 90% of the time he manages to live up to the ideal regardless. But then, like Eliot Spitzer, we find out about his loyal army of prostitutes.

This is one of my favorite strips. It's worth it just for the first panel, with Harry Potter and Aslan waiting at the bus stop. Where are they going? Why do they exist there? So many questions, and they'all have potentially hilarious answers.

At the time of this writing, I've dipped into this setting once more, with the release of *The Golden Compass* to theaters.

Optimus Primal and Megatron's gorilla vs. T-rex deal was based on the King Kong vs. T-rex brawl in the original *King Kong*. I can't source that specifically, but it's one of the possibly true trivia bits floating around in my brain.

Peter Jackson's *King Kong* came out on *Beast Wars*' tenth anniversary, so this double tribute strip was born.

I'm positive that the TBS comedy series *10 Items or Less* stole this joke from me.

Surprise! Just a homeless guy!

Robin's parents *probably* know she exists now. What with that thing that happens later. If not, maybe they should watch or read the damn news.

How big an *Animaniacs* dork am I? The only reason the Shortpacked books are in color is so that the Warner Brothers and Sister's noses can remain red, despite the sepia tone, just like in the show.

If you recognize everyone in the last panel, you've watched too much religious programming.

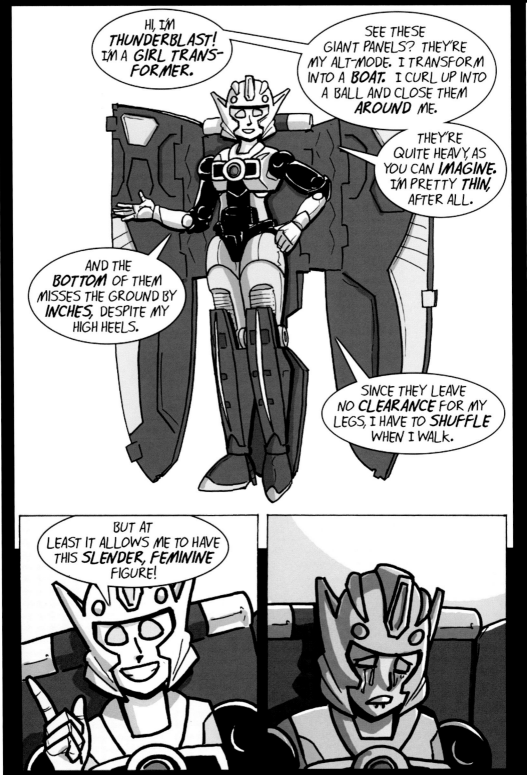

Thunderblast truly is one of the weakest Transformers in years. But she's a shapely girl, so people still like the toy for some reason. Hmm.

There's been several great fan-edits to this strip. One that comes quickly to mind involves Batman slowly turning transparent and ultimately disappearing starting in the fourth panel, leaving Commissioner Gordon bug-eyed.

This is all true.

Kermit was to be saying, "Oh, oh, a penguin. Oh."

Ask my friend Graham why.

I am such a bitch.

You *haven't* heard the last of Sydney Yus.

Honest.

See? There Ethan is again, assuming he's the good counterbalance to evil. He's kinda full of himself.

Amber's expression in the fourth panel is great. I should try that one again sometime.

THE DRAMA TAG

Despite that whole Faz thing, I thought I had the toystore thing down. There was a natural rhythm of the place that I was gettin' the hang of. Crap happens, Ethan gets in trouble, I laugh. Wash, rinse, repeat!

That's when things got weird.

There are things in this store that I just don't understand. So there's Galasso, right? He's our evil boss/dictator/The Cheese/whatever. But underneath all that brutal despot stuff, he's actually kinda offputting. He's a few marshmallows short of a marshmallow/steak sauce sandwich. And he brought Ronald Reagan back from the dead? How? And there's that whole thing with Mike.

There's seriously some shady stuff goin' on behind the scenes. Whenever I walk into the stockroom, the hairs on the back of my neck stand up. Total freakzone. You can almost hear somebody off in the distance whisperin' all "ch ch ch ah ah ah." Next time I totally do it with some hot dude, like with Ethan or something *fingers crossed*, I am so not going back there. You know how those movies go. Sluts get dead first.

(Amber is perpetually safe, I'm pretty sure.)

As long as I'm appearing pretty virginal, there's some really dark corners in there, so when I don't particularly feel like workin', they're a great place to hide.

But as I learned later, I don't seem to be alone in thinking that...

Uh oh, Robin's getting meta.

She pulled it and the strip didn't end on a joke! Oh shit. Oh shittily shit.

The blue box reads "Continued tomorrow" because *Shortpacked!* usually updates Monday-Wednesday-Friday, and would update all five weekdays during the duration of the Drama Tag storyline, and I wanted to tell people to come back the next day for more.

Amber's glasses were apparently genetically inherited.

I didn't honestly expect it to, but the "Hilarious!" narration box did seem to be rather funny, judging by the reactions of my readers. Weird. I wasn't planning on the narration boxes being a regular feature of the Drama Tag storyline, but this one sealed the deal. I just wanted an easy joke (or simulation thereof) at the end to maintain my street cred.

If you've read my previous work, *It's Walky!*, then you recognize that speech design.

This is about where people who dislike comic strip drama started *totally freaking out.* There are people who yell at me for doing comedy and people who yell at me for doing drama. Here's where I start playing with both sides.

He's the Head Alien, an old villain of mine. God, there's so much obvious real-world subtext here, and I manage to do all of it without breaching the fourth wall. How did I do this? (Lots of rewrites.)

Tits!

I usually draw *Shortpacked!* the day or so before the strip goes live, but for this storyline, I was excited enough about it to get a week or two ahead. This meant drawing far, far into the morning. But I couldn't stop. This is where the characters became real to me.

Underwear is required to be a hilarious color. It's a cartoon law.

This is another of my favorite *Shortpacked!* strips. One of my friends bought the original lineart from me because it is a work of crazy when there's no dialogue. I'd like to think it is framed on his wall, and when visitors drop by, they look at it and think *WHAT THE FUCK.*

Should I be assassinating Presidents in a comic strip? Doesn't that put me on some sort of government list?

I should probably stop borrowing the Q'ran from the public library.

I totally sold a lot of "Never presume a man does not have ninjas at his disposal" T-shirts.

Before this strip, I don't think you believed in Galasso or Ninja Rick. But now, suddenly, they have power.

All those items Robin wears are real, and we sold them at the Toys "R" Us I worked at. The chest symbol is a soundbox that, when the Batsymbol is pressed, Batman's voice proclaims, "Maybe one of my Batarangs will help!" And then you hear the whoopwhoopwhoop of the Batarang flying around, and then Batman shouts "UNGH!" He sounds for all the world like he just hit himself in the face with his own Batarang.

Batman even makes murder funny!

Yeah, that plastic isn't gonna stop a bullet, but Robin's... durable.

The medic in the last panel is based on Ratchet's holomatter avatar from IDW's *Transformers* comics.

And that first panel of Reagan sold me another buttload of T-shirts.

Amber and Ethan are getting coffee at the coffee shop from the webcomic *Questionable Content* (questionablecontent.net). They are also both wearing shirts that would eventually become real merchandise, just like the characters do in *Questionable Content*.

All in all, the Drama Tag storyline got me four T-shirt runs. Not bad.

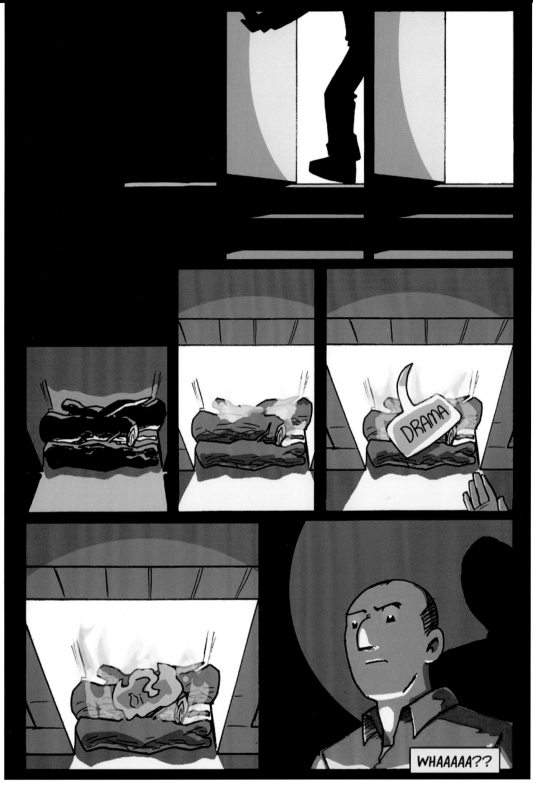

No comment.

In my "personal canon," I've furiously maintained that the *Teen Titans* cartoon takes place before *Batman: The Animated Series*. This strip was my way to link the two, solely for the benefit of my own amusement.

I think it's a tossup whether the "Batman DDR" strip (*Shortpacked! Brings Back the Eighties*, page 76) or this Frank Miller strip gets linked the most on other websites. I think lately this one's been edging out the ol' DDR standby.

See, everything he writes is about whores.

I've also heard of people claiming that Transformers reissues were shrunk, because they were WAY bigger when THEY were kids!

Hmm!

I was poking fun at legendary customizer Jin Saotome with this strip. He took it in good humor, and now we're pals. Since then, we've worked on a few customization projects together.

Look, God just wants more Scott Bakula, okay?

(Note that God speaks in the same font as Aslan.)

Everyone forgets about how they were totally right that one time. Ungrateful bastards we be.

Man, a Baroness toy without glasses is like *The Rocketeer* without Jennifer Connely. It's very interesting and exciting, but I'm just not going to get hard.

How's that for an out-there comparison? Did I do good?

Laugh at Greg Land all you want, but this was by far the hardest *Shortpacked!* strip to put together, by far.

Just like Greg Land, everyone here is traced from a photograph. But unlike Greg Land, I own up to it. Who did I trace? Answers are on page 132!

If I had a nickel for every time I heard this line while working retail, I'd be able to buy lots of sex from your mom.

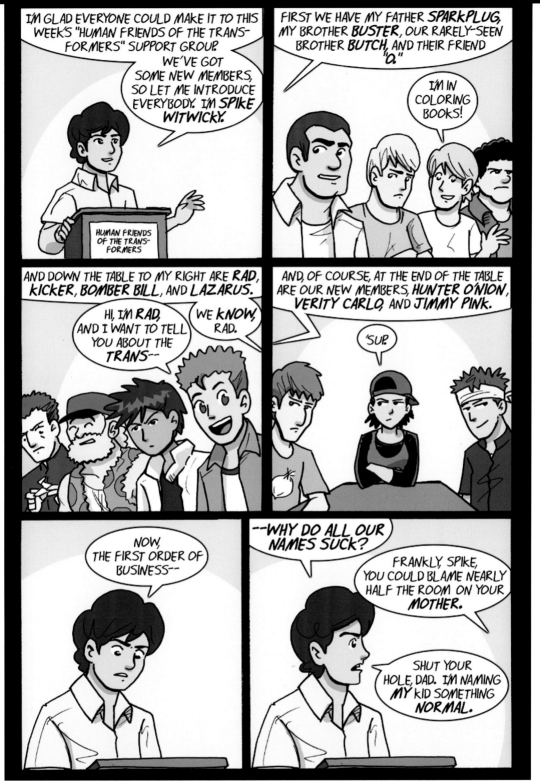

The live action *Transformers* movie was gracious, and gave us a protagonist named merely Sam. And *Transformers Animated* gave us a Sari. See? It's not so hard.

BRIDE OF FAZ

I think I've mentioned enough already how
naive our adorable little Amber is, but she doesn't
deserve to be hounded by that snot, Faz.

Even if she brings it on herself!

The saddest thing is that she, like many other
hot-things-in-training, is totally unaware how this
stuff works. If you ain't self-confident, you get the nerds and social failures.
If you're comfortable with the fact that the world ain't fit to lick the undersides
of your toes, then you'll get some quality man-age, the kind that ain't afeared
of a woman who knows her way 'round the town.

Glasses are a surefire road to Geek City man pickin's. You ever seen *Ugly
Betty*? I haven't, but I bet there's man-dorks downloading her every night.
(She's legal, right? I got no real idea.)

Meanwhile, the glasses-deprived Emma Watson is downloaded by real men.
Real pedophile men.

Hey, it's not her fault that "Hermione"
sounds like the thumpasprung sound
your bed makes while you're doin'
it.

Seriously, think about it.

*hermione hermione her-
mione hermione hermi-
one hermione hermi-
one hermione her-
mione hermione
hermione...*

This is how our kids
learn sex, folks.

The "mom who runs the register" can be seen briefly in the very first *Shortpacked!* strip.

Faz and I share woman-choosing criteria. I will narrow the field down to those who are shorter than me, thus enforcing an unspoken height-based dominion over her.

Also, I like a big rack.

This strip's last panel just broke my own brain. I should keep these strips fresher in my memory so they don't pounce on me like that.

What Robin says in the third panel is absolutely true, but we're not supposed to admit it.

See that bulging tummy? Yeah, that's right. Amber has a gut. Bet you won't see that in any other comic strip. Blondie? You could bounce pennies off those abs. Miss Buxley? She doesn't even have abs. Seriously, go look. She's a spine and skin. Cathy? .... okay, maybe Cathy has a gut.

Sometimes I feel I could really take Robin's advice in the first two panels. Damn my social phobias!

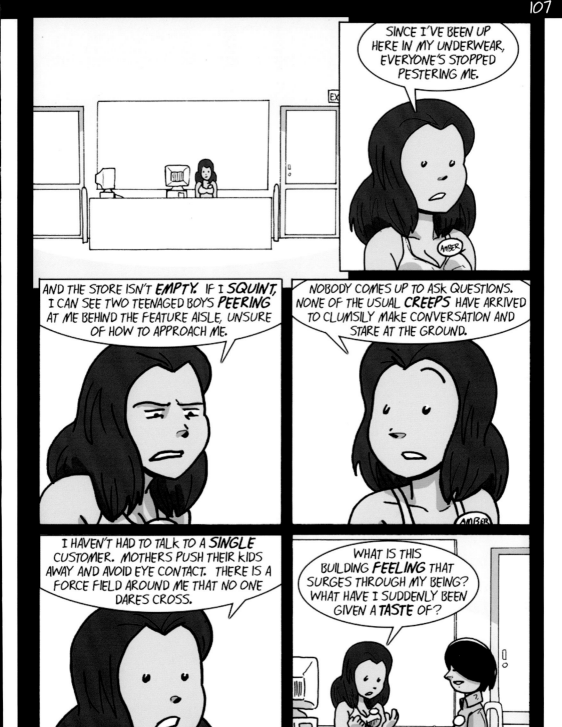

Power tastes like brownies, so I'm told.

I had a strip that followed this one that I rejected after sketching it in blue pencil, featuring Robin taking Amber shopping. However, it didn't really fit right, and I think Amber was beginning to wise up to Robin's antics too soon. Must artificially propel story forward!

It's too bad, because it involved butt-wiggling.

To me the second panel always looks too much like JonBenét Ramsey for comfort. Well, above the collarbone. Below that is all good.

Poor Galasso is so confused.

That's the thing that would kind of suck about being Adam and Eve. What if Adam is a total douche? You know, like a little naked douchey asshole? And it's not like Eve can tell Adam to go put some motherfreakin' pants on, because they haven't been invented yet.

Yet they must mate to continue mankind!

Hey, look, it's Eric Burns and Wednesday White! They (used to) write webcomics commentary. I forget exactly how this shameless cameo came into being, but I'm pretty sure it had something to do with the lure of hot lesbian makengs outs.

That's right. Eric Burns is eternally indebted to me.

I should start carrying around a tiny Kinsey Scale graph for just such situations. It would fold up and fit inside my wallet. What a conversation stopper!

Faz is clearly familiar with the tropes of this situation. If only one could do a musical montage in a webcomic...

Beast Machines came out on DVD that week. Can you tell?

God, there's so much recycled dialog in that show. It's ripe for drinking games. Take a drink if someone says "Music to my ears." Two drinks if someone shouts "Period!" Chug the whole thing if a single moment of joy occurs amidst the churning torrent of despair.

"Yeah, Mike, I'm no Predator. Predators make clk-clk-clk sounds and try their best to look like they're not a dude in a hokey costume."

Guys who like girls with low self esteem didn't really like this storyline.

Yeah, let's not pretend that we care.

Hey, can you tell that this strip was drawn on a crappy tablet PC? It looks like I drew it in the car.

This is one of the handful of strips I had to redraw after I had a harddrive failure. I traced it over the web-scaled version, so it didn't really change too much, and it did get rid of that drawn-on-tablet wobbly effect, so I guess it's all good.

This is the last time you see Amber's hair like this. It was a real pain to draw. I do kinda miss it, though. Maybe someday in the future I'll re-upgrade Amber's hair to "looking at all fashionable."

Robin, however, will be forever stuck wearing a pile of balloons on her head.

Toy News International strips

Long, long ago, the webmasters at *Toy News International* (toynewsi.com) approached me with the possibility of doing a weekly comic strip about toys for them. Well, hot dog, I thought! Embiggening! Expansion in mindshare! Hot babes!

I threw a "new" strip concept together, featuring myself, and deemed this new TNI-exclusive strip "Toy With Me," and *TNI* immediately but graciously declined.

So I ran crying to Adam Pawlus at *Entertainment Earth* (entertainmentearth.com), and they published the strip below in one of their quarterly catalogs.

But TNI came crawling back, just as I *knew they would*, and the concept was relaunched as a special weekend *Shortpacked!*. The strip I drew for the pitch was redrawn, replacing myself and my sweetie Maggie with Ethan and Amber, I changed the name of the toy mentioned in the strip (from Jetfire to Soundwave, I believe) to make it feel more current, and *Shortpacked!* weekly at *Toy News International* began!

I really wish I had the original David/Maggie version of this strip, to offer a comparison, but I am lame and I lost it. This is a special book compilation, dammit! It's like Michael Bay forgot to film his filming of his explosions for the DVD special features. Only with less Awesome! involved.

Shortpacked!'s *TNI* strips are an entirely different exercise than the normal full-page variety. A four-panel gag has a different comedic timing than one in six or eight. It opened me up to new kinds of *Shortpacked!* gags, plus it kept a toy-themed *Shortpacked!* strip going weekly while I indulged myself and my readers in bouts of semi-dramatic storylines in the main strip.

I used to do this all the time. I knew it wouldn't work, but a desperate man does not do rational things.

Another thing to do is to take toys off the pegs and hide them in other aisles in the store, to hopefully trick the stockpeople into thinking they need to put out new product.

1980s *G.I. Joe* collectors will try to fit the 3-3/4" figures into any vehicle. You should have seen them when the 2.5"-scale *Sigma Six* stuff came out. The old stuff *had to fit*. It just *had to.*

Bumblebee's movie face was so frightening that the film achieved only #3 at the box office instead of #1.

It was 2006. At least one *Snakes on a Plane* joke was required per webcomic.

And thus Ethan died via skull trauma.

You know what I want to see? *Star Wars Guess Who?*.

"Is your guy an alien?" "Yes." "Does your guy have some manner of tentacles extruding from his head?" "No." "Does your guy have a butt for a face?" "Yes." "Is your guy Ponda Baba?"

Way back in the first book, I did a strip about Batman being able to breathe in space. The toy that strip was lampooning came with a little lenticular image of Batman fighting Darkseid (in space) that Batman could hold. Why? Who the hell knows. Maybe Batman's insecure.

Transformers Classics Megatron is awesomely fun. At first I was disappointed that there weren't any electronics, but as this strip demonstrates, it's much more fun to make your own.

Recent pop culture has really warped our perception of the word "classic." I think I once saw a commercial advertising "classic" episodes of *Two and a Half Men*.

Behind the scenes

Preliminary Shortpacked! sketches

As my previous webcomic, It's Walky! was ending, I began sketching ideas for my next webcomic series. One of my first ideas involved Robin, the ex-government agent, and her misadventures with this shmuck she runs into, named Ethan. The conceit of the series was that so long as Robin was around Ethan, Ethan had incredibly terrible luck, and immediately, due to a mishap, Ethan found himself wanted by the insane mobster, Galasso. Hijinx ensue!

When I decided to do a toy store thing instead, I kept most of the character concepts I'd developed, including Robin, Ethan, Galasso, and their bookish galpal Amber, but transplanted them.

To the right and below are several design sketches for Ethan and Amber. I really had trouble settling on a hairstyle for Amber. There's a few here that I really really like, but couldn't get to look good from other angles.

Amber's hairstyle continued to fluctuate up to the beginning of the comic strip itself, and even then went through some variations, as thumbing through these book collections will attest.

Below is an old **"Shortpacked 1.0"** strip I accidentally left out of Book One. It, uh, gets crammed here for lack of a better placement.

Maybe I'm just super-lonely, but that Scarlett bust is really frickin' hot. I don't even LIKE Scarlett all that damn much.

Let me tell you your problem. Take a good look at the proportions of that bust.

GI JOE

An adult's torso is three heads tall. That thing's torso is only two heads tall.

What are you hinting at?

You're a pedophile.

Robin was introduced first in *It's Walky!*, my webcomic before *Shortpacked!*. She was a hyperactive speedster who fought aliens for the government. I created her there with the intention of carrying her over into whatever my next webcomic series would be when *It's Walky!* ended.

Here are some early concept sketches for her. You can tell she is zany because she wears *sandals*.

Below is her first appearance in *It's Walky!*, published August 26, 2003. In subsequent installments, Joyce would remark that Robin "smells like Skittles."

On the following pages are concept sketches for the cover of this book. I started with a straightforward *Star Wars* parody and then scaled it back to an homage.

Greg Land cheat sheet!

Hey, look, it's all the photographs I traced for my Greg Land strip! (page 97) You'll notice that Ethan is always Jason Biggs while Amber is apparently a mix of Allison Mack and Alicia Silverstone. Now, if I were truly aping Greg Land, I probably should have made sure to use a different celebrity every panel. Oh well.

I like how Jason Biggs is crushing that swimsuit model's head.

You too can have your own Drama Tag, just like Robin! Just cut along the dotted line, wave your Drama Tag about, and bear witness to the hackneyed melodrama that ensues!

We the People

of the United States, in Order to form a more perfect Union, establish Justice, insure domestic Tranquility, provide for the common defence, promote the general Welfare, and secure the Blessings of Liberty to ourselves and our Posterity, do ordain and establish this Constitution for the United States of America.

Article 1

ABOUT THE AUTHOR

David Willis is no stranger to the world of webcomics, having started his first series, *Roomies!*, in 1997. Including *Roomies!*, he has four webcomics series under his belt, such as the sci-fi drama *It's Walky!*, its more domestic sequel *Joyce and Walky!*, and *Shortpacked!*, a look at action figures and pop culture. In 2005, he and other leading cartoonists formed the webcomics collective Blank Label Comics.

Raised in La Porte, Indiana, David Willis graduated from the Illinois Institute of Art in Schaumburg, Illinois with a Bachelor in Fine Arts. After college, he escaped the frighteningly-empty cornfields and hicks of Indiana to the frighteningly-empty cornfields and hicks of Ohio.

David Willis currently resides in Columbus, Ohio, where he surrounds himself with more Transformers toys than he can bother to count.